Writing Center P

Shape Stationery with
Writing Prompts and Story Starters

Written by Sue Lewis and Rozanne Lanczak Williams

Editor: Vicky Shiotsu
Illustrators: Terri Rae and Karen Hanke
Cover Photographer: Michael Jarrett
Designer: Karen Hanke
Cover Designer: Barbara Peterson
Art Director: Tom Cochrane
Project Director: Carolea Williams

Table of Contents

7. Sparkling Star

10. Radiant Rainbow

13. Lively Leaf

16. Adorable Apple

19. Snazzy Schoolhouse

22. Helping Hand

25. Bookworm Book

28. Darling Doll

31. Busy Bus

34. Sweet Snowman

37. Marvelous Mitten

40. Happy Heart

43. Fragrant Flower

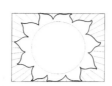

46. Summer Sun

49. Delightful Dog

52. Cuddly Cat

55. Clever Cow

58. Precious Pig

61. Friendly Frog

64. Bubbly Bird

67. Merry Mouse

70. Awesome Ant

73. Bashful Bug

76. Beautiful Butterfly

79. Silly Spider

82. Brave Bear

85. Enormous Elephant

88. Opulent Octopus

91. Wonderful Whale

94. Dapper Dinosaur

Writing Center Prompts

Introduction

There is nothing worse for young writers (or any writer) than staring at a blank sheet of paper and not knowing where to begin. As a teacher, you most likely have heard students complain, "I don't know what to write about!" One way you can inspire children to write is by providing them with lots of modeling and encouragement, along with motivational ideas to spark their imaginations and get their creative juices flowing.

Writing Center Prompts is a resource that will help you to create an exciting writing center in your classroom. You'll find great story ideas and prompts, writing frames, and related book titles that will inspire even the most reluctant writer. The writing ideas allow children to work at their own level and pace, experience success in a variety of writing formats, and develop confidence in their writing ability.

How to Use This Book

Writing Center Prompts is filled with special stationery your students will love! Thirty fun shapes are presented with three pages for each shape—a writing ideas page, a blank shape page, and a lined shape page.

Writing Ideas Page

This page includes a list of books related to a particular theme, several story starters and prompts, and one or two writing frames. Here are some suggestions for using each section.

- *Literature Connection*
  The books listed in this section are perfect for reading aloud and for inspiring your class to write a variety of stories, poems, or letters to book characters. Keep these books (and others that have the same theme) in a tub at the writing center, along with the shape stationery.

- *Story Ideas and Prompts*
  Several writing prompts are provided to encourage students to try different forms of writing, including narrative, descriptive, expository, persuasive, and creative writing. At least one prompt for each shape is directly related to a book in the Literature Connection. Look for these icons before the prompts, and use them to create a balanced writing program:

  N Narrative Writing   **D** Descriptive Writing

  E Expository Writing   **P** Persuasive Writing

  C Creative Writing

How can you get your students to write? The key is to provide plenty of modeling. Before assigning children to the writing center, explain the writing prompts carefully, and do several examples together. In addition, create word lists and encourage students to refer to a classroom word wall when they write independently.

- *Writing Frames*
  One or two open-ended writing frames are provided to support beginning writers. More experienced writers will enjoy using the frames as springboards for their own ideas.

The frames can be used in a variety of ways:
- Write the frame on a chart and have students copy the frame and fill it in with their own words.
- Write the frame on the shape before reproducing it. Estimate how much room students will need. Some frames are long and may not fit on one page, so you may need to write out the frame over several pages.
- Write the frame on regular lined paper, so students have more space to write. Students can use the shape as a cover for their "book."

Using the Shape Pages

Blank Shape Pages

The uses for these charming pages are endless!
The fun shapes will enliven and enhance the writing
activities for students. The pages can be used as is,
or individual shapes can be cut out. Here are some
suggestions:

- Have students write directly on the shapes to display stories, poems, and other writings.
- Have students use the pages to illustrate their writing.
- Create shape books. Use one of the pages for a cover, and then staple the student's work together.
- Let students use the pages to write themed book reviews.
- Staple together several seasonal pages (such as the snowman) to create a seasonal journal for each student.
- Have students copy poems on the pages, and place the pages in a box to make a classroom poetry collection.
- Use appropriate shapes (such as the apple, star, sun, or heart) for letting students create concrete poems.
- Use the pages to write notes or invitations to parents.
- Write notes of praise or encouragement, and pass them out to every student.
- Write phonics words on related shapes (such as short *a* words on the cat shape or *ar* words on the star shape), and let students use the words for word work.
- Use the shapes as patterns for art projects or room decorations.
- Use the pages for creating worksheets.
- Use the pages to write weekly or monthly newsletters.

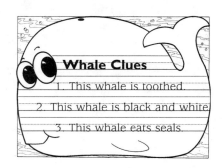

Lined Shape Pages

The lined shape pages are ideal for all writing activities
as well as handwriting practice.

Sparkling Star

Literature Connection
- *Draw Me a Star* by Eric Carle
- *The First Starry Night* by Joan Shaddox Ison
- *Laura's Star* by Klaus Baumgart
- *Twinkle, Twinkle, Little Star* by Iza Trapani

Twinkle, twinkle, little star!

Are you close or are you far?

I will make a wish tonight.

Twinkle, twinkle, shine so bright!

Story Ideas and Prompts

C Place gold or silver star stickers on black paper to create a constellation. Write a story telling how the constellation was formed in the sky.

E Write a report about stars. Here are some questions you might answer:
– *Why do stars twinkle?*
– *Why can't stars be seen during the day?*

N After reading *Laura's Star*, write a story about your own special star. Use star stickers to decorate the story.

D What makes you special? What makes you a star? Write about your "star qualities"!

C Read Iza Trapani's version of *Twinkle, Twinkle, Little Star*. Write a new version of the song.

Writing Frames

A Shining Star

_____ is a shining star!
_____ is a star because _____.
Here are the ways this "star" shines bright:
_____.
_____.

Star Light, Star Bright

Star light, star bright,
I will make a wish tonight.
I wish _____.
I wish _____.
I wish _____.
And I wish my wishes come true!

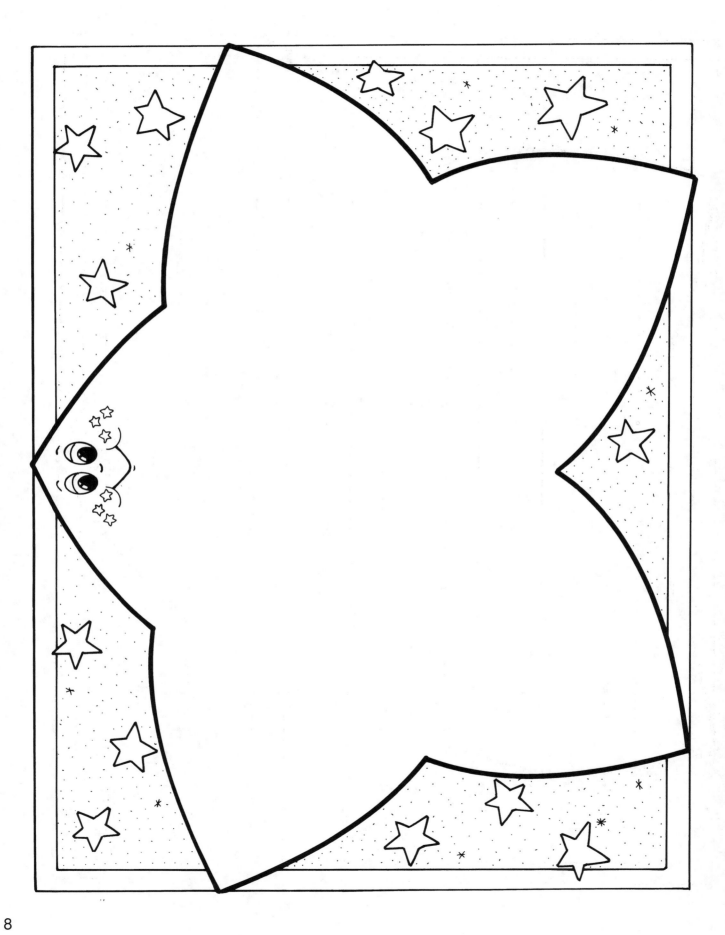

8

Radiant Rainbow

Literature Connection
- *All the Colors of the Rainbow* by Allan Fowler
- *Listen to the Rain* by Bill Martin Jr. and John Archambault
- *Moonbear's Skyfire* by Frank Asch
- *Rain* by Robert Kalan

Story Ideas and Prompts

N People used to say that a pot of gold could be found at the end of a rainbow. Write about what you would like to find at the end of a rainbow.

P Write about all the different kinds of weather you have where you live. Tell which kind of weather you like best.

C Create a color poem. On each line, write about a different color of the rainbow.

E After reading *Moonbear's Skyfire*, write a letter to Bear telling him why the thing he saw in the sky was not a fire that he had to put out.

Writing Frame

Rain

Rain on the _____,
Rain on the tree,
Rain on the _____,
But not on me!

Rain on the _____,
Rain on the sea.
Rain on the _____,
But not on me!

Red is a dripping, frosty cherry Popsicle.
Orange is a refreshing glass of juice.
Yellow is the slippery yolk of an egg.
Green is a soft bed of grass.
Blue is the sky and sea.
Purple is a violet.

12

Lively Leaf

Literature Connection
- *From Seed to Plant* by Gail Gibbons
- *The Giving Tree* by Shel Silverstein
- *Red Leaf, Yellow Leaf* by Lois Ehlert
- *A Tree Is Nice* by Janice May Udry
- *We Can Eat the Plants* by
  Rozanne Lanczak Williams

Orange
is the color of
big, fat
pumpkins.
Red is the color of juicy
apples.
Yellow is the color of
corn.
Brown is the color of
crunchy leaves.

Story Ideas and Prompts

D Describe a food that comes from a plant.

C Sponge-paint a blank leaf shape with fall colors. Then write a poem about fall colors on a lined leaf shape.

P Read *A Tree Is Nice*. Write why you think a tree is nice.

Summer Tree Song

The shade from the
green tree
Is all I need,
I'll sit right here and
Read, read, read!

D Create a leaf book. Glue different kinds of leaves to the pages, and write a description of each one.

C Write song verses about leaves or trees during different seasons.

Writing Frame

Fall Five Senses

I see _____.
I hear _____.
I feel _____.
I smell _____.
I taste _____.
I know the season is _____!

Fall Five Senses

I see colorful leaves
falling.
I hear crunchy leaves
when I walk.
I feel chilly air.
I smell apple pie baking.
I taste yummy Halloween
candy.
I know the season is
fall!

Adorable Apple

Literature Connection

- *Apples* by Gail Gibbons
- *How to Make an Apple Pie and See the World* by Marjorie Priceman
- *The Seasons of Arnold's Apple Tree* by Gail Gibbons
- *The Story of Johnny Appleseed* by Aliki

Story Ideas and Prompts

C Work in groups of four. Each person gets a blank apple shape and draws or paints an apple tree in the spring, summer, winter, or fall. Label the pictures. Afterwards, write a group story about a changing apple tree.

P Use a blank apple shape to create a "Good Apple Award" for a deserving person—perhaps the student of the week or a classroom volunteer. Write a paragraph telling why this person deserves an award.

E Have an apple-tasting party in class. Sample as many different kinds of apples as possible. Then create a graph showing which apples your class liked best.

E Write the directions for your favorite apple recipe. Draw a picture to go with it. Bind all the recipes together to create a classroom cookbook.

D Some people go apple picking in the fall. Describe your favorite fall activity.

Writing Frame

Nature's Gift

Write a haiku about apples.

Line 1: 5 syllables
Line 2: 7 syllables
Line 3: 5 syllables

Nature's Gift
Crunchy, crisp apples,
Growing on a pretty tree,
Let's make applesauce!

Writing Center Prompts © 2001 Creative Teaching Press

Snazzy Schoolhouse

Literature Connection

- *Huggly Goes to School* by Tedd Arnold
- *Miss Bindergarten Gets Ready for Kindergarten* by Joseph Slate
- *My Teacher's My Friend* by P. K. Hallinan
- *School* by Emily Arnold McCully
- *This Is the Way We Go to School* by Edith Baer

Story Ideas and Prompts

C Write at least three "Very Cool School Rules."

P Write a letter inviting your family to a school event (Back-to-School Night, Open House, or a special performance or meeting).

D Write a letter to a pen pal in another class or school. Describe your classroom or your school.

C On a blank schoolhouse shape, draw a friendly monster or creature. Then write a story about what happens when the monster or creature visits your school.

N Write a paragraph about the first time you went to school.

Writing Frame

My School

The name of my school is _____.

My teacher's name is _____.

Other people who help me at school are _____.

At school I like to learn about _____.

If I could change my school, I would _____.

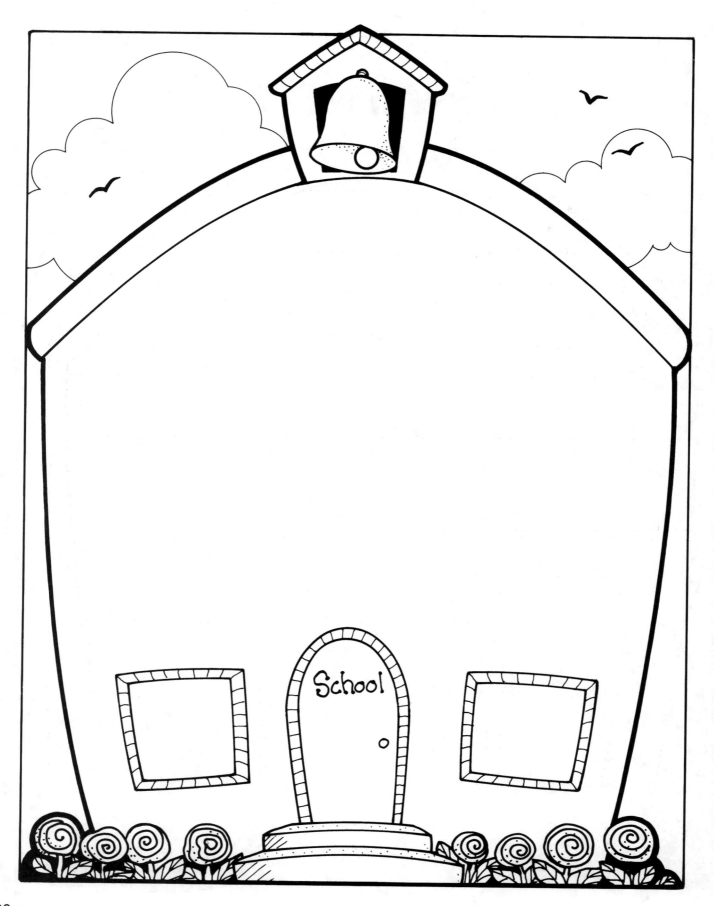

School

Writing Center Prompts © 2001 Creative Teaching Press

Helping Hand

Literature Connection

- *Grandma's Hands* by Dolores Johnson
- *The Handmade Alphabet* by Laura Rankin
- *Here Are My Hands* by Bill Martin Jr. and John Archambault
- *If You Were a Construction Worker* by Virginia Schomp
- *Whose Hat?* by Margaret Miller

Story Ideas and Prompts

D Interview a school helper. Write and illustrate a paragraph about that helper.

C Write a story about a superhero with giant hands.

D Read *Here Are My Hands*. Describe how you use your hands. Tell how you use your hands to wave hello or good-bye, shake hands, and so on.

D Copy a blank hand shape onto card stock. Gather small textured items (such as cotton balls, sandpaper, ribbon, and terry cloth). Glue an item on the tip of each finger. Write a word that describes each object. Then write sentences on lined paper describing how each item feels.

Cotton balls are soft and fluffy. Sandpaper feels rough and scratchy.

Writing Frame

I Can Be a Helper

I can help at home. I can _____.

I can help at school. I can _____.

I can help my friend. I can _____.

I can help in my neighborhood. I can _____.

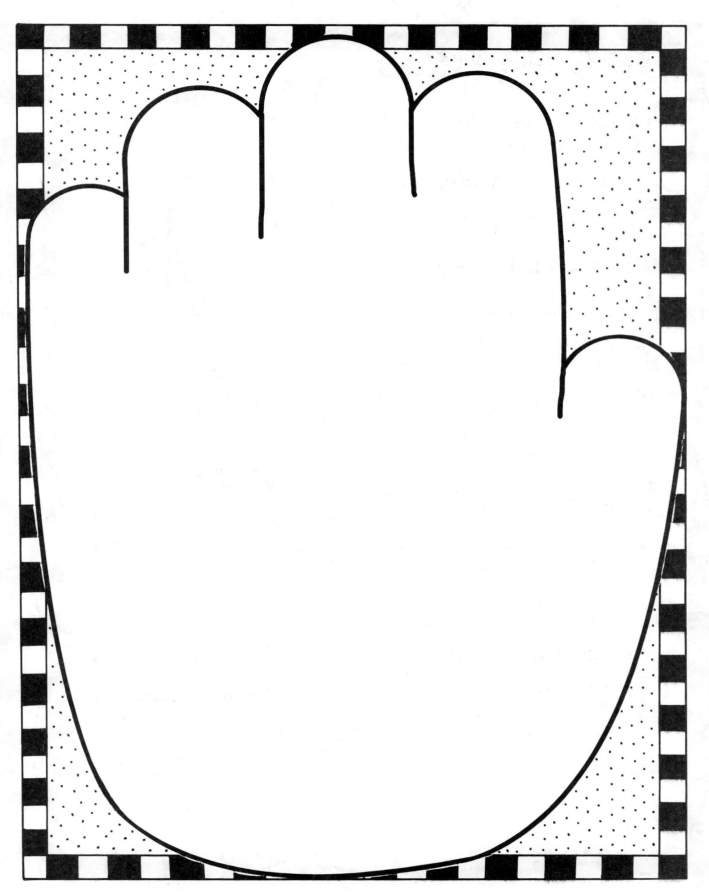

24

Bookworm Book

Literature Connection

- *How a Book Is Made* by Aliki
- *Petunia* by Roger Duvoisin
- *The Wednesday Surprise* by Eve Bunting
- *What Do Authors Do?* by Eileen Christelow
- *Wolf!* by Becky Bloom

Story Ideas and Prompts

C Pretend that you are a character in your favorite book. What would you do differently? How would your story be different from the original?

D Describe a book you wish someone would write.

E Create a story map of a book you just read.

P Write a book review. Tell whether or not children your age would enjoy the book.

C Write a new ending for a favorite story.

N Imagine that you have just written a book. Write a paragraph titled "Meet the Author" for the back cover. Include at least three interesting facts about yourself.

If I were Pinocchio, I wouldn't want to be a real boy. I'd rather stay a puppet and not worry about chicken pox, colds, cuts, and broken bones. I'd help make other puppets too.

Writing Frame

My Book Report

Title _____

Author _____

Illustrator _____

Characters _____

What Happened _____

I liked/did not like this book because _____.

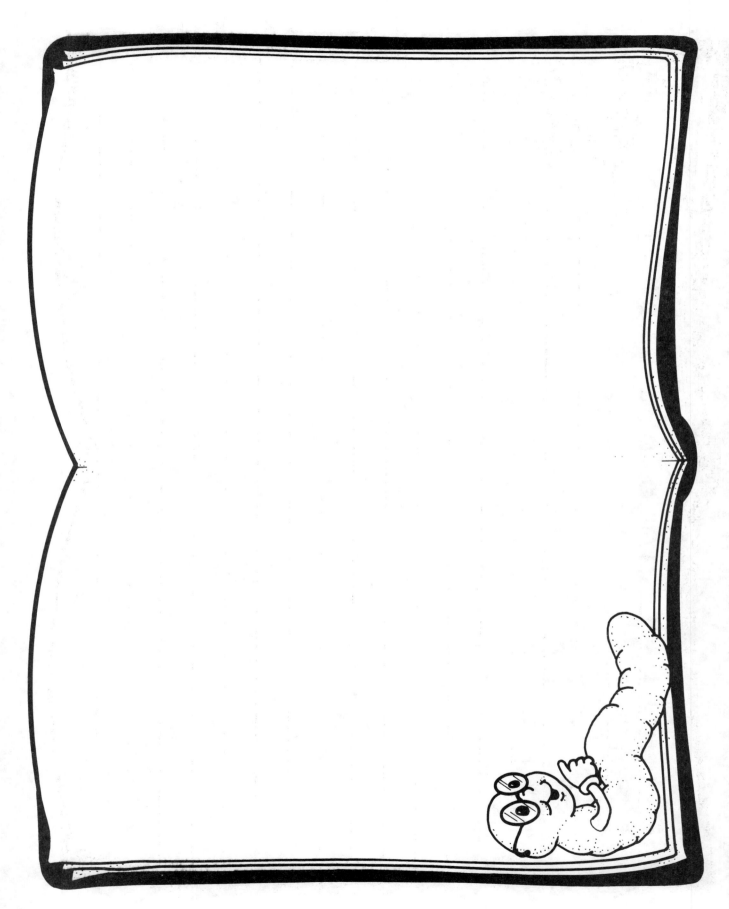

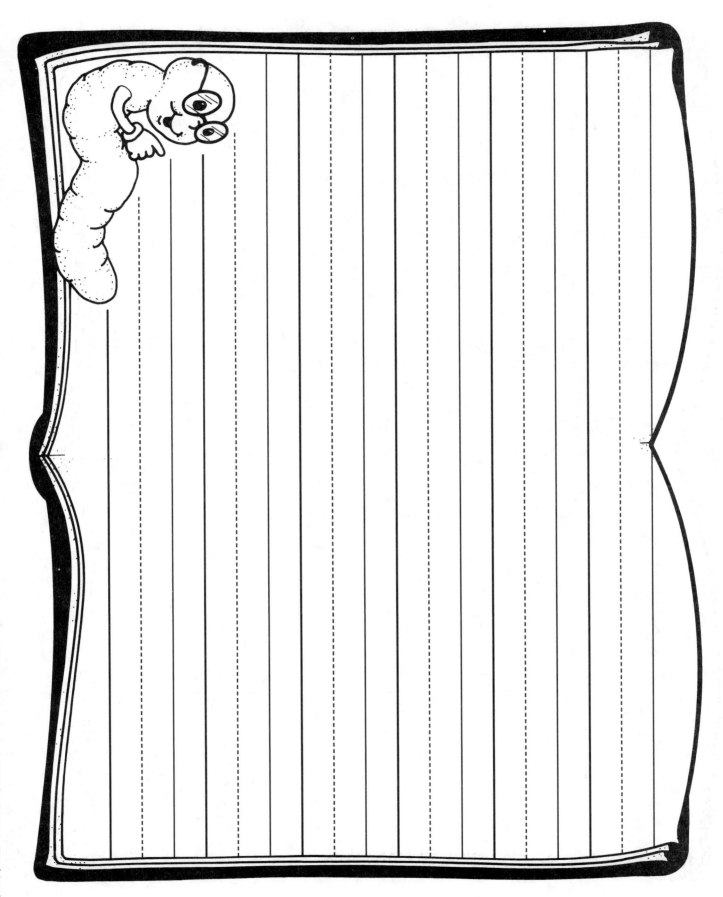

Darling Doll

Literature Connection

- *Best Friends* by Steven Kellogg
- *Children Just Like Me Celebrations* by Anabel Kindersley
- *Chrysanthemum* by Kevin Henkes
- *I Like Me!* by Nancy Carlson
- *I'm Terrific* by Marjorie Weinman Sharmat
- *Ruby the Copycat* by Peggy Rathman

Story Ideas and Prompts

My favorite book character is Madeline. She's smart and funny!

D Decorate a doll shape as a favorite book character. Then describe the character on lined paper.

N Suppose you are writing to a pen pal for the first time. Write a paragraph introducing yourself.

C Write a poem telling what you think you will be doing five years from now.

D Write a paragraph describing the qualities that one needs to be a good friend.

P After reading *Chrysanthemum*, write why you think your name is special.

Writing Frame

All About Me!

My name is _____.

I am _____ years old.

I like to _____.

I like to _____, too.

I have a special family. They are _____.

Something I do very well is _____.

I am a good friend when I _____.

30

Busy Bus

Literature Connection
- *Bus Stop* by Taro Gomi
- *Magic School Bus* series by Joanna Cole
- *Riding the Bus with Mrs. Kramer* by Alice Flanagan
- *This Is the Way We Go to School* by Edith Baer
- *The Wheels on the Bus* by Raffi

Story Ideas and Prompts

C Write a new verse to "Row, Row, Row Your Boat," focusing on a different kind of transportation.

N Imagine you could hop aboard the Magic School Bus with Ms. Frizzle! Write a new adventure.

D After reading *This Is the Way We Go to School*, describe how you get to school each day.

Ride the Bus

Ride, ride, ride the bus,
Ride it to your school.
Climb aboard the yellow bus,
Riding the bus is cool!

E Write about the different types of transportation you use in one week.

P Write about the kind of person who would make a good school bus driver.

Writing Frame

On the Go!

I go to _____.
I get there by/in _____.
I go to _____.
I get there by/in _____.
I go to _____.
I get there by/in _____.

On the Go!

I go to school.
I get there by walking.
I go to the mall.
I get there in my mom's van.
I go to my grandma's.
I get there by plane.

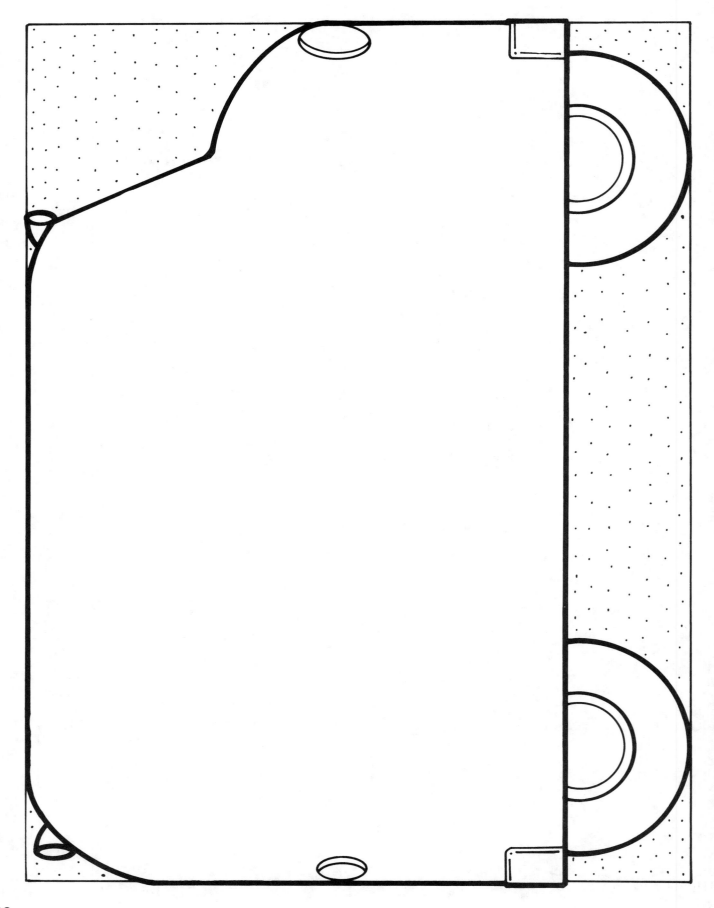

Sweet Snowman

Literature Connection
- *The Mitten* by Jan Brett
- *The Snowman* by Raymond Briggs
- *A Snowman Named Just Bob* by Mark K. Moulton
- *The Snowman Who Went for a Walk* by Mira Lobe
- *The Snowy Day* by Ezra Jack Keats

Story Ideas and Prompts

D Describe your favorite winter activity.

N Read *The Snowy Day*. Then write how you would spend a snowy day. Tell about your activities in the order you would do them, explaining what you would do first, second, and so on.

E Write directions for building a snowman.

C Write a poem about the best snowman you ever built.

C Write a story about a special place where snowmen go for the summer.

My snowman is cheery.
My snowman is big.
My snowman is jolly and nice.
My snowman is funny.
My snowman is happy.
My snowman loves snow and ice!

Writing Frames

My Snowman

My snowman is _____.
My snowman is _____.
My snowman is _____ and _____.
My snowman is _____.
My snowman is _____.
My snowman _____!

My Snowlady

My snowlady's name is _____.
My snowlady's name has _____.
My snowlady is _____.
My snowlady can _____.
I like my snowlady!

Marvelous Mitten

Literature Connection

Froggy Gets Dressed by Jonathan London
The Jacket I Wear in the Snow by Shirley Neitzel
The Mitten by Jan Brett
The Mystery of the Missing Red Mitten by Steven Kellogg
"The Three Little Kittens" (a Mother Goose nursery rhyme)

Story Ideas and Prompts

C Read *The Mitten*. On a lined mitten shape, write your own version of the story. For instance, write about another animal who tries to get into the mitten. Then cut out and decorate two blank mitten shapes and staple them together, leaving the cuff open. Use this mitten as a prop and share your story.

D Write directions describing how you would dress to go out on an icy cold and snowy day.

C On a lined mitten shape, write new verses for the tune "Muffin Man" titled "Mitten Man" or "Mitten Miss" *(Do you know the mitten man, the mitten man, the mitten man? Oh, do you know the mitten man, who lives on North Pole Lane?).*

P Decorate a pair of blank mitten shapes with a partner. Together, write an advertisement that tells people why your mittens are the best.

Wonderful Winter

Let's build a snowman.
Let's build it together.
This is what we do
In cold and snowy weather.

Writing Frame

Wonderful Winter

Let's _____.
Let's _____ together.
This is what we do
In _____ and _____ weather.

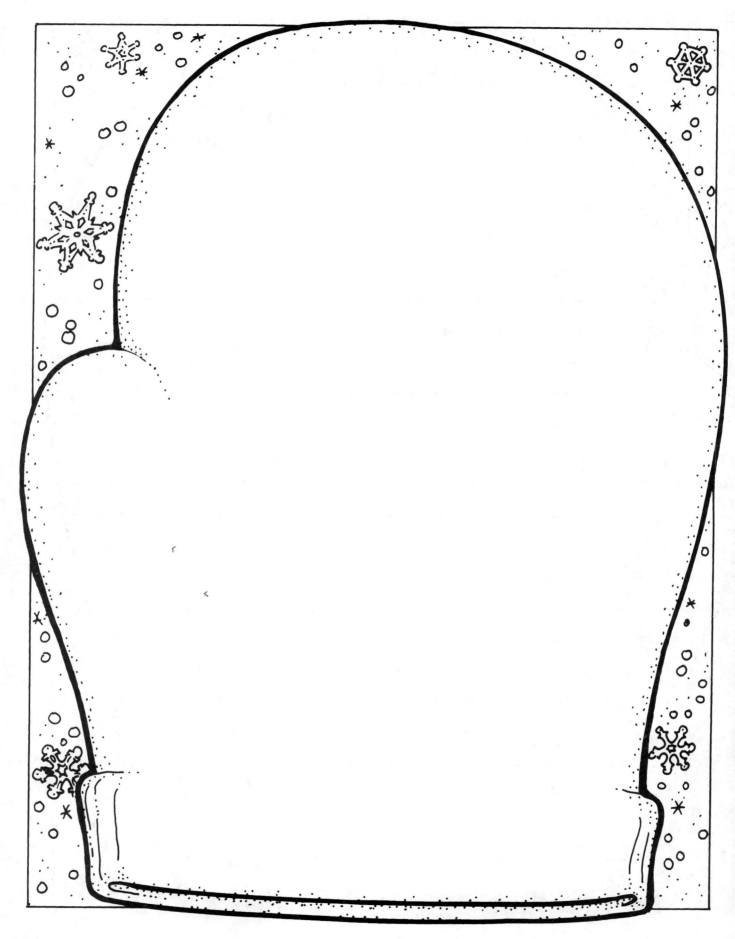

38

Happy Heart

Literature Connection

- *Best Friends* edited by Lee Bennett Hopkins
- *Friends* by Helme Heine
- *Frog and Toad* series by Arnold Lobel
- *George and Martha* series by James Marshall
- *Somebody Loves You, Mr. Hatch* by Eileen Spinelli

Story Ideas and Prompts

C Write an acrostic poem about someone special. Use the letters in the person's name to begin the lines.

Lisa
Likes to play games.
Is fun to be with.
Shares with me.
Always has good ideas.

E Read *Somebody Loves You, Mr. Hatch.* Then write a letter to someone special or someone who is feeling lonely. Don't sign the letter—deliver the letter secretly!

C Write a "recipe" for making a lasting friendship.

N Did someone ever surprise you with "a random act of kindness"? Tell about that special time.

D Write about three gifts you could give your family that wouldn't cost any money. Describe why you would give them.

Writing Frame

Friends

What do friends do?
They _____.
They _____.
They _____, too.
They _____.
They _____.
That's what friends do!

Friends

What do friends do?
They walk to school with you.
They play with you.
They tell great jokes, too.
They share.
They care.
That's what friends do!

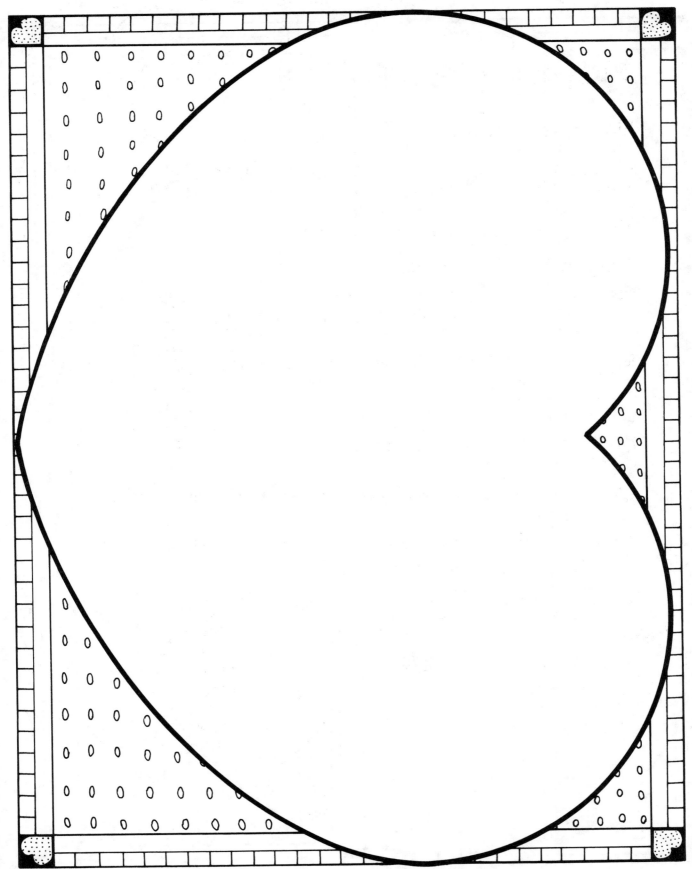

Fragrant Flower

Literature Connection

- *From Seed to Plant* by Gail Gibbons
- *Miss Runphius* by Barbara Cooney
- *The Reason for a Flower* by Ruth Heller
- *Spring Is Here* by Taro Gomi
- *The Tiny Seed* by Eric Carle

Story Ideas and Prompts

C Write a poem or paragraph telling the "reason for a flower." *(Flowers make the world more beautiful. Flowers make people smile. Flowers help bees make honey.)*

C How do you know it's spring? Write a poem called "Signs of Spring."

E Write a paragraph explaining how a tiny seed grows into a flower.

D Draw a flower. Then write at least five words or phrases describing it.

Good-bye, Winter! Hello, Spring!
Good-bye, snow.
Hello, rain.
Good-bye, jacket and boots.
Hello, shorts and T-shirts.
Good-bye, bare trees and
gray sky.
Hello, sun and flowers.
Good-bye, Winter!
Hello, Spring!

Writing Frames

Good-bye, Winter! Hello, Spring!

Good-bye, _____.
Hello, _____.
Good-bye, _____.
Hello, _____.
Good-bye, _____.
Hello, _____.
Good-bye, Winter!
Hello, Spring!

Spring Is Here!

Spring is here. Spring is here.

How do you think I know?

I see (smell, hear. . .)_____.

I know it must be so!

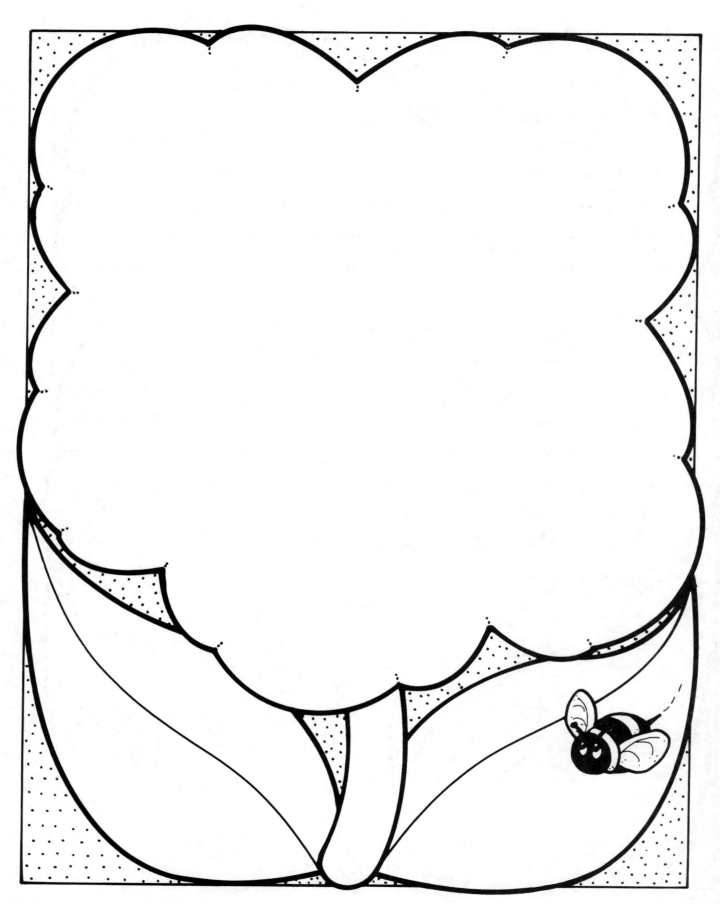

44

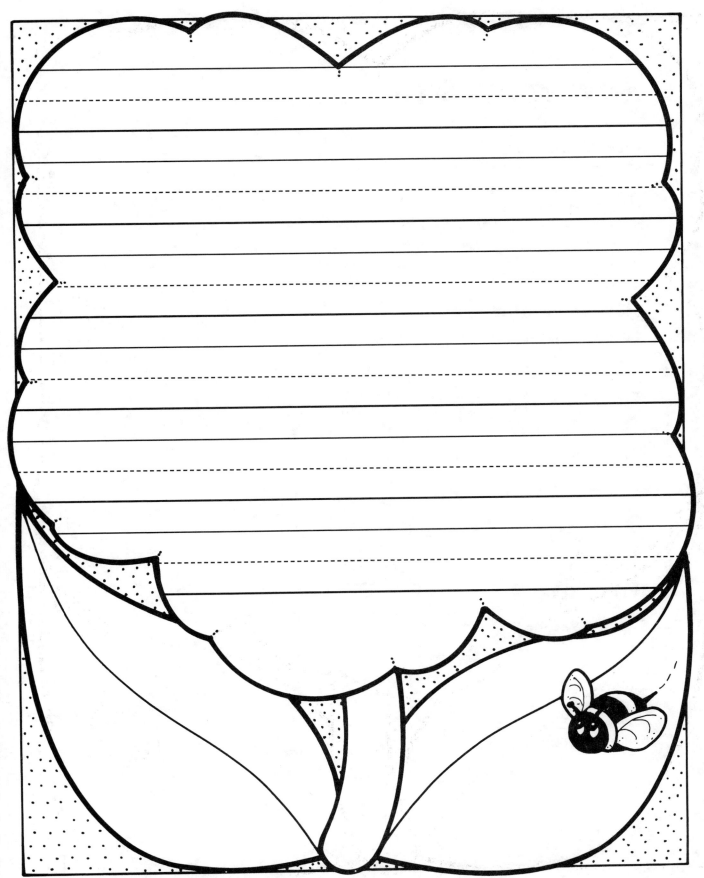

Summer Sun

Literature Connection

- *Greetings, Sun* by Phillis Gershator, et al.
- *How I Spent My Summer Vacation* by Mark Teague
- *Hurry Granny Annie* by Arlene Alda
- *Lemonade Sun: And Other Summer Poems* by Rebecca Dotlich
- *Sun Up, Sun Down* by Gail Gibbons
- *Time of Wonder* by Robert McCloskey

Story Ideas and Prompts

C Write a poem titled "Hurray for Summer Vacation!"

D After reading poems from *Lemonade Sun*, describe your own ideas of what summer is. Draw pictures to go with your work.

N Tell about the best summer vacation you ever had. Or, write a story about a perfect summer vacation.

E Write a paragraph titled "Sunsational Facts About the Sun."

Writing Frame

Summer Vacation

A time to _____.
A time to _____.
A time to _____.
A time to _____.
A time to _____.
Summer vacation is _____!

Hurray for Summer Vacation!

*Hurray for no more homework,
No more shoes,
Warm sunshine.
Hurray for summer vacation!*

Summer Vacation

*A time to sleep in.
A time to read.
A time to jump in the pool.
A time to skateboard.
A time to play baseball.
Summer vacation is cool!*

Writing Center Prompts © 2001 Creative Teaching Press

Delightful Dog

Literature Connection

- *Any Kind of Dog* by Lynn Reiser
- *Clifford the Big Red Dog* series by Norman Bridwell
- *Dog Heaven* by Cynthia Rylant
- *Harry the Dirty Dog* by Gene Zion
- *Henry and Mudge* series by Cynthia Rylant

Story Ideas and Prompts

P Do dogs make the best pets? Write your opinion.

E Pretend you are writing a pet care manual for dog owners. What are four tips you would include in your book?

C Create a cartoon strip featuring a dog.

D Describe your dog or write about a dog you would like to have.

D What makes a dog happy? Describe at least three things.

D Suppose you could create a park for dogs. Write what you would put in it.

I think dogs make the best pets. They are fun to play with. They are loyal friends. Dogs let you know they are happy to see you.

Writing Frame

My Dog

My dog is _____.
My dog is _____.
My dog loves _____ and _____.
My dog can _____.
My dog has _____.
I love my dog!

My Dog

My dog is white.
My dog is fluffy.
My dog loves walks and food.
My dog can smile.
My dog has a wet tongue.
I love my dog!

Cuddly Cat

Literature Connection
- *Barn Cat* by Carol P. Saul
- *Cookie's Week* by Cindy Ward
- *Have You Seen My Cat?* by Eric Carle
- *Mama Cat Has Three Kittens* by Denise Fleming
- *Rotten Ralph* series by Jack Gantos

Story Ideas and Prompts

C Make a list of words that rhyme with *cat*. Then use the words to write silly rhymes.

E Write a recipe for the perfect cat food.

C Read several books about Rotten Ralph. Write another story about Ralph that shows just how rotten he can be!

C Write and illustrate an ABC book about cats.

P Do cats make the best pets? Write your opinion.

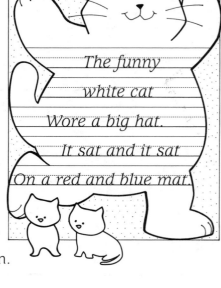

The funny
white cat
Wore a big hat.
It sat and it sat
On a red and blue mat.

Writing Frame

My Cat

As _____ as a _____,
As _____ as a _____,
As _____ as a _____,
Is my sweet little cat!

My Cat

As soft as a pillow,

As quiet as a snowfall,

As fun as a birthday party,

Is my sweet little cat!

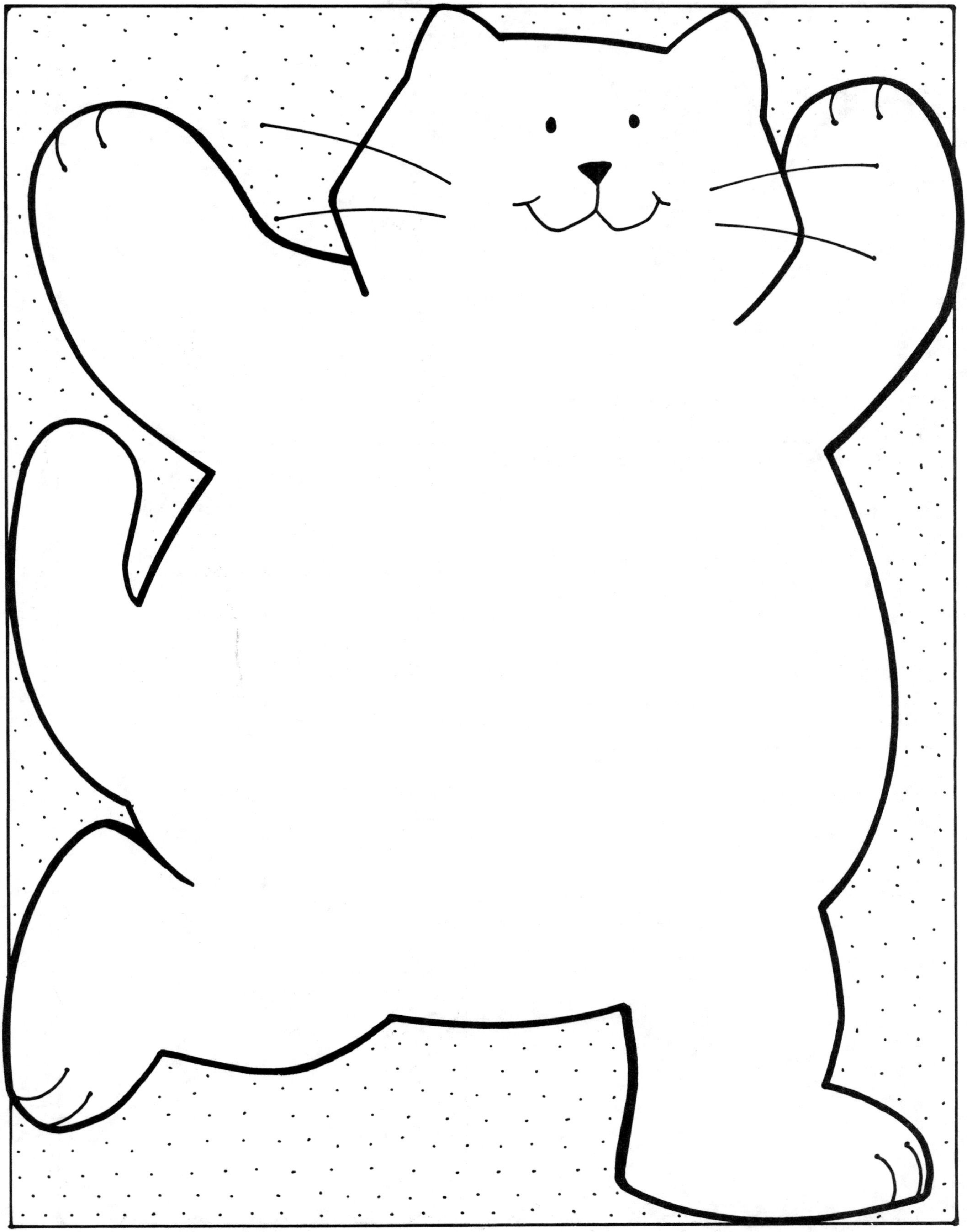

54

Writing Center Prompts © 2001 Creative Teaching Press

Clever Cow

Literature Connection
- *The Big Red Barn* by Margaret Wise Brown
- *The Cow Buzzed* by Andrew Zimmerman and David Clemesha
- *Milk: From Cow to Carton* by Aliki
- *One Cow Moo Moo* by David Bennett
- *The Story of Ferdinand* by Munro Leaf

Story Ideas and Prompts

E Imagine that you are a reporter and have just interviewed the cow who jumped over the moon in the famous nursery rhyme "Hey Diddle Diddle." Write a newspaper article describing the interview.

E Write a report explaining how milk gets from the cow to your refrigerator.

D Suppose you were a cow in need of a home. Write a want ad describing the type of place you are looking for and the type of person you would want as your owner.

C Write a new verse for the song "The Farmer in the Dell." *(The farmer feeds the hogs, the farmer feeds the hogs . . . .)*

C Write a new verse for "Old MacDonald Had a Farm," featuring things found on a farm besides animals. *(Old MacDonald had a farm, E-I-E-I-O. And on this farm he had a barn, E-I-E-I-O. With a barn door here, and a pile of hay there. . . .)*

Guess Where I Am
I see crops growing in the field.
I hear "Moo, moo!"
I smell hay.
I taste sweet, juicy apples.
I touch a soft baby chick.
Guess where I am.
I'm on a farm!

Writing Frame

Guess Where I Am

I see _____.
I hear _____.
I smell _____.
I taste _____.
I touch _____.
Guess where I am. I'm on a farm!

55

Precious Pig

Literature Connection
- *The Book of Pigericks* by Arnold Lobel
- *If You Give a Pig a Pancake* by Laura J. Numeroff
- *Piggies* by Audrey and Don Wood
- *Pigs* by Robert Munsch
- *Pigs Will Be Pigs* by Amy Axelrod
- *Small Pig* by Arnold Lobel
- *Ten Dirty Pigs/Ten Clean Pigs* by Carol Roth

Story Ideas and Prompts

C Make a list of words that begin with *p*. Use a dictionary to help you. Then write some tongue twisters that feature pigs.

C Write your own version of "This Little Piggy." *(This little piggy played baseball. This little piggy fell asleep on the rug. This little piggy rolled in the mud. This little piggy baked cookies. And this little piggy went wiggly, wiggly, wiggly all the way home!)*

P Pretend you are a pig. Write why you enjoy mud so much.

C Read *The Book of Pigericks* by Arnold Lobel. Then try writing a few pigericks of your own.

Playful pink pigs make perfect playmates. Petunia Pig packed peas and peppers for a picnic.

Writing Frame

Pigs

Pigs get so dirty.
When they _____,
When they _____,
And when they _____.
Pigs get so clean.
When they _____,
When they _____,
And when they _____.

Pigs
Pigs get so dirty.
When they roll in the mud,
When they eat too fast,
And when they splish
and splash.
Pigs get so clean.
When they take bubble baths,
When they take showers,
And when they roll in
the flowers.

Writing Center Prompts © 2001 Creative Teaching Press

Friendly Frog

Literature Connection

- *Frog and Toad* series by Arnold Lobel
- *Frog Counts to Ten* by John Liebler
- *The Frog Prince* by Edith H. Tarcov
- *Froggy* series by Jonathan London
- *Jump, Frog, Jump!* by Robert Kalan
- *Ready, Set, Hop!* by Stuart J. Murphy

Story Ideas and Prompts

E Write about the life cycle of a frog. Illustrate the different stages.

P Would you like a frog for a pet? Write why or why not.

C Read *The Frog Prince*. Then write a new ending for the story.

C Read *Frog Counts to Ten*. Then write your own clever counting book.

C Read one or more books from Arnold Lobel's *Frog and Toad* series. Then draw a Venn diagram comparing and contrasting Frog and Toad. Write a short story about the two characters.

Little Green Frog

*Boing, boing! went
the little green frog one day.
Boing, boing! went the little green frog.
Boing, boing! went
the little green frog one day,
And he boing, boing,
boinged away.*

Writing Frames

Frog and Toad

A _____, _____ frog came out one day.
It _____, then hopped away.
A _____, _____ toad came out one day.
It _____, then hopped away.

Little Green Frog

_____, _____! went the little green frog one day.
_____, _____! went the little green frog.
_____, _____! went the little green frog one day,
And he _____, _____, _____ away.

62

Bubbly Bird

Literature Connection

- *Across the Stream* by Mirra Ginsburg
- *Feathers for Lunch* by Lois Ehlert
- *Feathery Facts* by Ivan Chermayeff
- *Goose* by Molly Bang
- *Hey, Al* by Arthur Yorinks
- *Wow! It's Great Being a Duck* by Joan Rankin

Story Ideas and Prompts

D Make up an imaginary bird. Give it a name and write a description of it.

The Ooh-Ooh Bird

The ooh-ooh bird is so pretty that people say, "Ooh! Ooh!" when they see it. The bird has blue feathers. Its wings are tipped with gold and silver. Its tail is long and curly.

E "Birds of a feather flock together." Write what you think this proverb means.

P In the book *Hey, Al*, a man and his dog almost turn into birds. Would you like to be a bird? Write why or why not.

E Think of a bird. Write three or more facts about it without telling its name. See if someone can guess the bird.

D Suppose you could fly like a bird. Write where you would go. Describe how it feels to fly.

Writing Frame

Birds

There are many kinds of birds.
Some are _____ and some are _____.
Some live in _____ and
some live in _____.
Some make _____ noises and
some make _____ noises.
I wonder what the world would be like without birds!

I would like to be a bird, because I would like to fly. Flying would make me feel free!

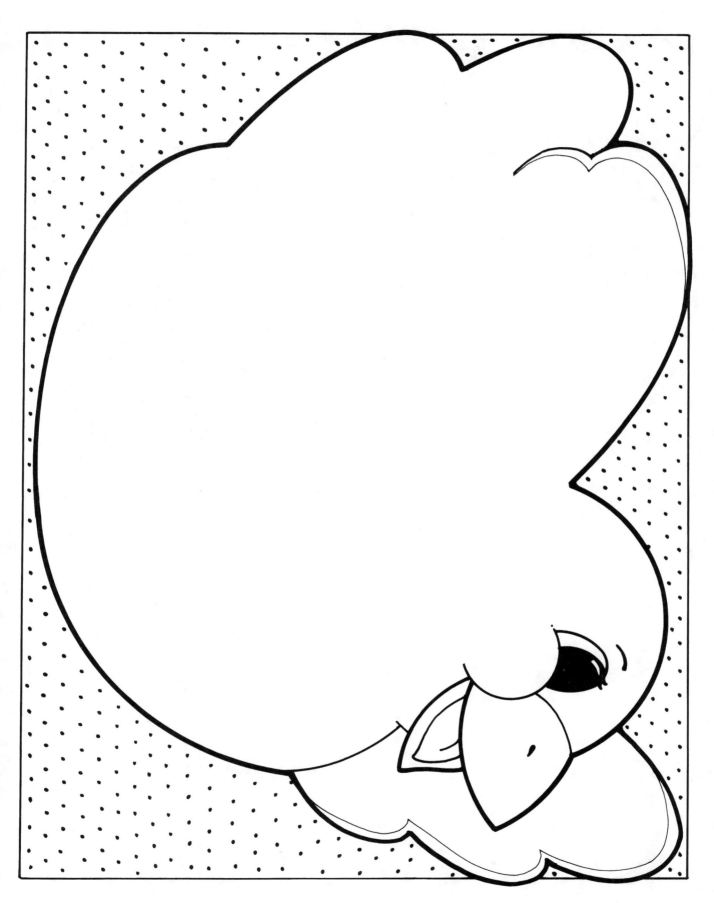

Merry Mouse

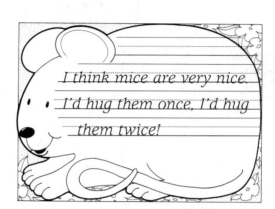

Literature Connection

- *If You Give a Mouse a Cookie* by Laura J. Numeroff
- *Mouse Paint* by Ellen Stoll Walsh
- *Mouse Tales* by Arnold Lobel
- *Mouse Views* by Bruce McMillan
- *Seven Blind Mice* by Ed Young

Story Ideas and Prompts

C Make a list of words that rhyme with *mice*. Use the words to write rhyming couplets (a pair of lines of verse that rhyme) about mice.

I think mice are very nice.
I'd hug them once, I'd hug them twice!

C Write your own version of *If You Give a Mouse a Cookie*. (*If you give a mouse new shoes, then she will want to go to the movies. When you get to the movies, the mouse will want popcorn . . . .*)

P Read *Seven Blind Mice*. Which mouse was the smartest? Write your opinion.

Writing Frame

Three Little Mice

Three little mice,
Hiding in a shoe,
One _____,
And then there were two.

Two little mice,
Hiding from the sun,
One _____,
And then there was one.

One little mouse,
Seeing day was done,
It _____,
And then there were none!

Three Little Mice
Three little mice,
Hiding in a shoe,
One took a nap,
And then there were two.

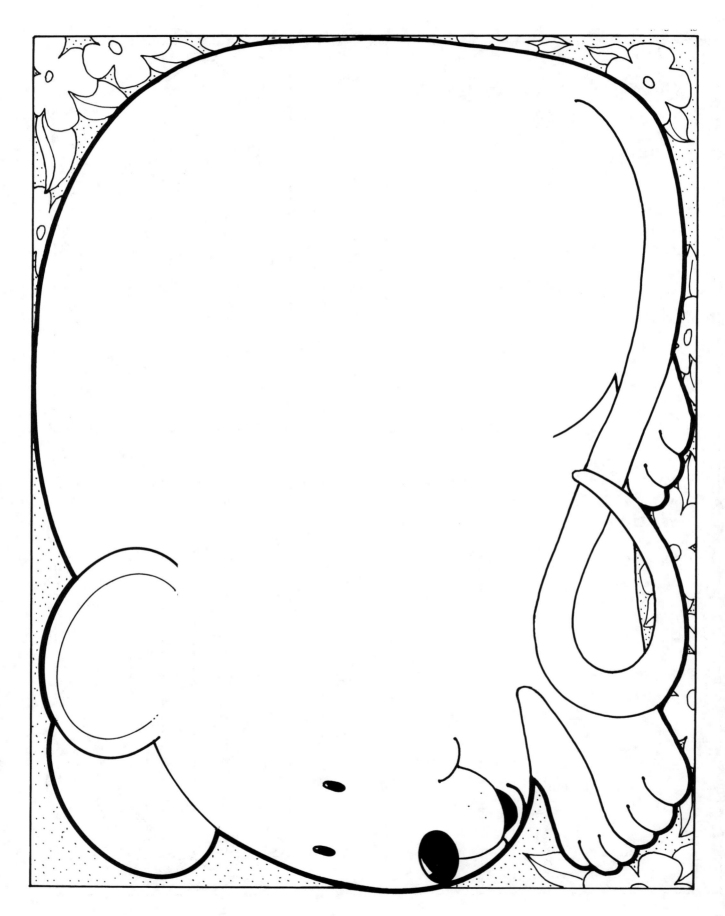

Writing Center Prompts © 2001 Creative Teaching Press

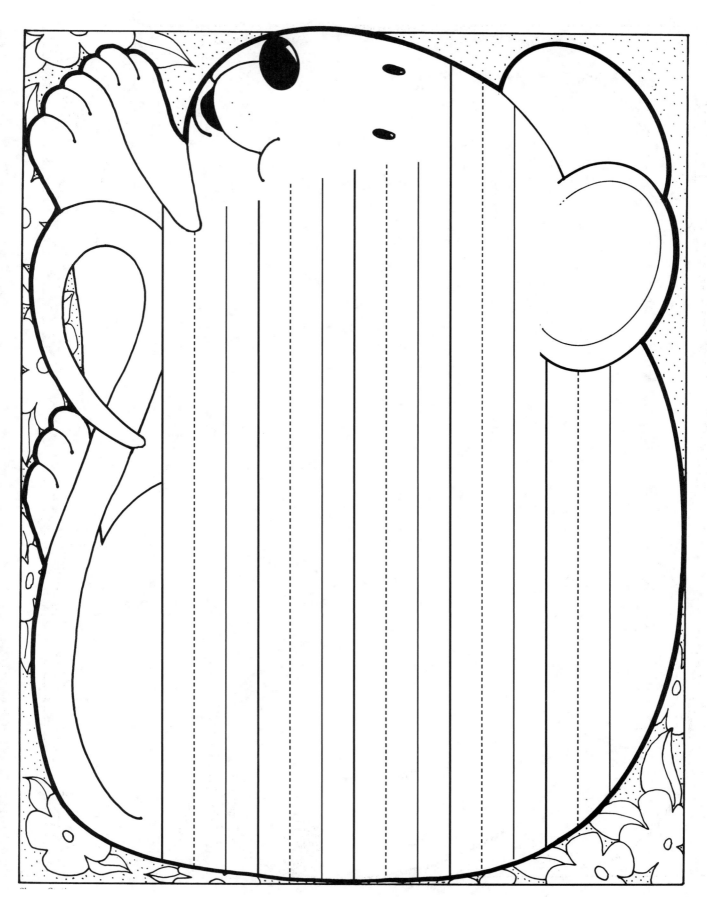

Writing Center Prompts © 2001 Creative Teaching Press

Awesome Ant

Literature Connection
- *The Ant and the Elephant* by Bill Peet
- *Hey, Little Ant* by Philip and Hanna Hoose
- *One Hundred Hungry Ants* by Elinor Pinczes
- *There's an Ant in Anthony* by Bernard Most
- *Two Bad Ants* by Chris Van Allsburg

Story Ideas and Prompts

D Suppose you were an ant. Describe what one of these things would look like to you: a blade of grass, a rock, a crust of bread.

E Write a science report titled "Amazing Ants."

C Using an ink pad, make some thumbprint ants. Write a story about your ants.

C Read *Two Bad Ants*. Then write another adventure for the two bad ants.

P Pretend you are an ant. Write a speech that will persuade people not to step on you.

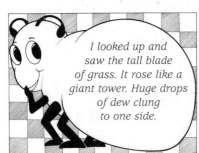

I looked up and saw the tall blade of grass. It rose like a giant tower. Huge drops of dew clung to one side.

Writing Frame

The Ants Go Marching

The ants go marching one by one.
The _____ one stops to _____.

The ants go marching two by two.
The _____ one stops to _____.

The ants go marching three by three.
The _____ one stops to _____.

(Continue the verses as desired.)

The Ants Go Marching
The ants go marching one by one. The biggest one stops to have some fun.

Bashful Bug

Literature Connection

- *The Best Bug Parade* by Stuart J. Murphy
- *Bugs! Bugs! Bugs!* by Bob Barner
- *Flit, Flutter, Fly!* edited by Lee Bennett Hopkins
- *I Like Bugs* by Margaret Wise Brown
- *Snug Bug's Play Day* by Cathy East Dubowski and Mark Dubowski

Story Ideas and Prompts

C Read several bug poems like the ones in *Flit, Flutter, Fly!* Then try writing one of your own.

C Use the names of insects to make rhyming couplets. *(I saw a bee. It smiled at me.)*

C Write an insect riddle. First, draw an insect on a blank bug shape. Then, write three clues about your insect on a lined bug shape. Staple the lined shape over the blank one.

A bumblebee buzzed,
A dragonfly flew,
They waved and said,
"How do you do?"

D Make an ABC book describing bugs.

Writing Frame

I Like Bugs

I like bugs!

_____ bugs,
_____ bugs,
_____ bugs!
Any kind of bug!

A bug in _____,
A bug on _____,
A bug by _____,
I like bugs!

I Like Bugs
I like bugs!
Wiggly bugs,
Fuzzy bugs,
Spotted bugs,
Any kind of bug!

Beautiful Butterfly

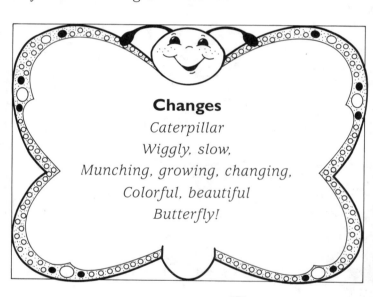

Literature Connection

- *The Beautiful Butterfly: A Folktale from Spain* by Judy Sierra
- *How to Hide a Butterfly & Other Insects* by Ruth Heller
- *I Wish I Were a Butterfly* by James Howe
- *The Very Hungry Caterpillar* by Eric Carle
- *Where Does the Butterfly Go When It Rains?* by May Garelick

Story Ideas and Prompts

D Read *Where Does the Butterfly Go When It Rains?* Describe and illustrate an interesting place for a butterfly to hide during a rainstorm.

E Explain the life cycle of a butterfly in words and pictures.

C Imagine the most beautiful butterfly in the world. Write a poem describing it.

D A caterpillar looks very different from the butterfly it will become as an adult. Think about what you will look like as an adult. Write how you will change. Write how you will stay the same.

Changes

Caterpillar
Wiggly, slow,
Munching, growing, changing,
Colorful, beautiful
Butterfly!

Writing Frame

Changes

Caterpillar
Wiggly, _____,
Munching, _____, _____,
Colorful, _____,
Butterfly!

Silly Spider

Literature Connection

- *Be Nice to Spiders* by Margaret Graham
- *How Spider Saved Halloween* by Robert Kraus
- *The Itsy Bitsy Spider* by Iza Trapani
- *Spider on the Floor (Raffi Songs to Read)* by Bill Russell and True Kelly
- *The Very Busy Spider* by Eric Carle

Story Ideas and Prompts

C Write a different version of the nursery rhyme "Little Miss Muffet."

C Write a spooky spider story.

C Read and sing Raffi's *Spider on the Floor*. Then write your own lyrics to the song.

*Little Miss Muffet sat
under a tree,
Eating her sandwich and pie.
Along came a spider
Who sat down beside her,
And made
Little Miss Muffet cry!*

P Some people are afraid of spiders. Do you think spiders are scary? Write why or why not.

D Go on a spider safari. Find a spider, observe it carefully, then write a description of it.

Writing Frames

There's a Spider

*There's a spider on/in the _____,
Oh, my!
There's a spider on/in the _____,
Oh, why?
There's a spider, I just spied her,
On/in the _____, on/in the _____,
There's a spider on/in the _____,
Good-bye!*

All About Spiders

*Spiders have _____,
Spiders have _____,
Spiders are _____,
Spiders are _____,
Spiders _____,
Spiders _____.*

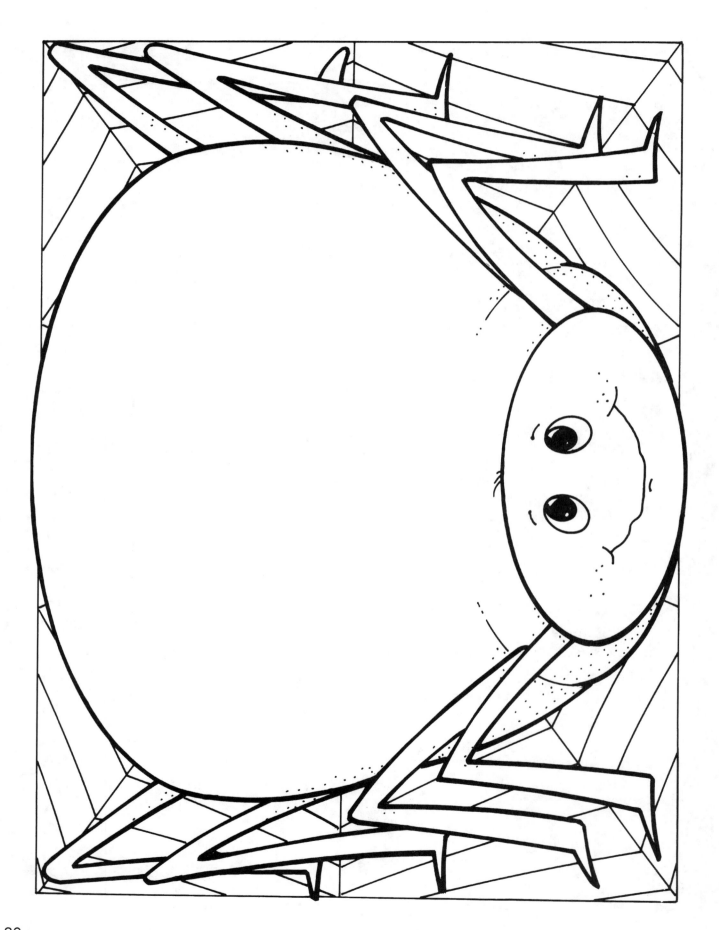

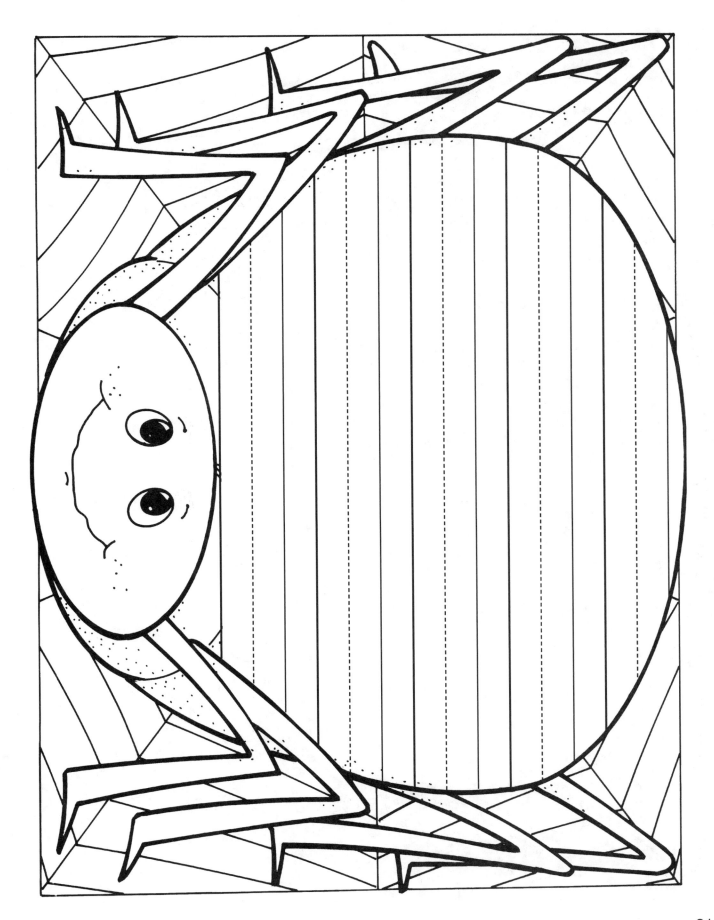

Brave Bear

Literature Connection

- *Good as New* by Barbara Douglass
- *Ira Sleeps Over* by Bernard Waber
- *Jesse Bear, What Will You Wear?* by Nancy White Carlstrom
- *Little Bear* series by Else Holmelund Minarik
- *Where's My Teddy?* by Jez Alborough

Story Ideas and Prompts

C Write and sing your own verses to the song "The Bear Went Over the Mountain." *(The bear went on vacation . . . to get a little rest.)*

D Use construction paper scraps, ribbon, and other materials to "dress up" a blank bear shape. Then describe your bear on lined paper, and tell where he or she is going in the new outfit.

N Write a story about your favorite teddy bear or other stuffed toy.

E Write five interesting facts about bears.

Bears, Bears

Bears, bears,
Bears climb stairs.
Bears, bears,
Bears eat pears.
Bears, bears,
Bears wear red.
Bears, bears,
Bears jump on my bed!

Writing Frames

All Kinds of Bears

_____ *bears,*
_____, _____ *bears,*
_____, _____, _____, *bears,*
_____, _____ *bears,*
_____ *bears,*
All kinds of bears!

Bears, Bears

Bears, bears,
Bears _____.
Bears, bears,
Bears _____.
Bears, bears,
Bears _____.
Bears, bears,
Bears _____!

Enormous Elephant

Literature Connection
- *The Elephant's Child* by Rudyard Kipling
- *Five Minutes' Peace* by Jill Murphy
- *Hiccups for Elephant* by James Preller
- *The Right Number of Elephants* by Jeff Sheppard

Story Ideas and Prompts

C Read *The Right Number of Elephants*. Then write a new page for the book.

D In the book *Hiccups for Elephant*, all the animals try to cure Elephant of a bad case of hiccups. Describe your own original cure for hiccups.

E Draw a Venn diagram comparing the Asian elephant with the African elephant. Then write a paragraph telling how they are alike and how they are different.

D Describe what you would do if you had to hide an elephant.

If you need to reach the cookie jar on the top shelf, then the right number of elephants is ONE. If you want to have a parade, then the right number of elephants is FIVE.

Writing Frames

Elephants
Elephants are _____.
Elephants are _____.
Elephants have _____.
Elephants eat _____.
Some elephants _____.
Some elephants _____.
But all elephants _____.

If I Had a Pet Elephant
If I had a pet elephant,
I would _____.
If I had a pet elephant,
I would take it to _____.
If I had a pet elephant,
I would give it _____.
If I had a pet elephant,
I would feel _____.

Writing Center Prompts © 2001 Creative Teaching Press

Opulent Octopus

Literature Connection

- *Herman the Helper* by Robert Kraus
- *My Very Own Octopus* by Bernard Most
- *Rainbow Fish* by Marcus Pfister
- *Sea Creatures with Many Arms* by D. M. Souza
- *Sea Sums* by Joy N. Hulme

Story Ideas and Prompts

P After reading *My Very Own Octopus*, write about why it would be good or bad to have an octopus as a pet.

N Write a story about what would happen if you woke up one day and found that you had eight arms!

C Write a poem about a visit to the aquarium.

E Write a report about a sea animal.

P Suppose you could turn into a sea animal. Write which animal you would like to be and why.

Under the Sea

What do I see under the sea?

A shark swimming,

A jellyfish floating,

A dolphin diving,

A crab crawling.

That's what I see under the sea!

Writing Frame

Under the Sea

What do I see under the sea?
A _____ swimming,
A _____ floating,
A _____ diving,
A _____ crawling.
That's what I see under the sea!

Writing Center Prompts © 2001 Creative Teaching Press

Wonderful Whale

Literature Connection
- *Baby Beluga (Raffi Songs to Read)* by Raffi
- *Baby Whale* by Lynn Wilson
- *Big Blue Whale* by Nicola Davies
- *Whale Song* by Jennifer Hopson
- *Whales* by Gail Gibbons

Story Ideas and Prompts

E On a blank whale shape, draw a picture of one kind of whale. Label your picture. On a lined shape, write three or four clues. Staple the clues on top of the picture. See if someone can read your clues and guess what kind of whale it is.

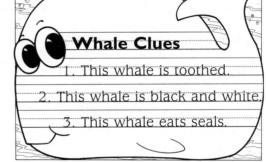

Whale Clues
1. This whale is toothed.
2. This whale is black and white.
3. This whale eats seals.

C Write a tall tale with a whale as the main character. Title your story "A Whale of a Tale."

E Read and sing Raffi's *Baby Beluga*. Then find out about beluga whales. Write at least three interesting facts about them.

C The blue whale is the largest animal that ever lived. If you could talk to a blue whale, what three questions would you ask it? Write how you think the whale would answer.

Writing Frame

Whale

(Two words describing a whale)
(Three words describing a whale's actions)
(Four words expressing a feeling about a whale)
(One or more words that stand for whale)

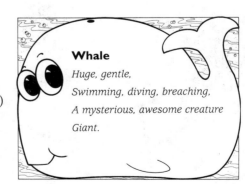

Whale

Huge, gentle,
Swimming, diving, breaching,
A mysterious, awesome creature
Giant.

Dapper Dinosaur

Literature Connection

- *Danny and the Dinosaur* by Syd Hoff
- *Digging Up Dinosaurs* by Aliki
- *Dinosaur Bob* by William Joyce
- *Dinosaurs* by Gail Gibbons
- *Dinosaurs, Dinosaurs* by Byron Barton
- *If the Dinosaurs Came Back* by Bernard Most

Story Ideas and Prompts

D Read *If the Dinosaurs Came Back*. Describe another way that dinosaurs could be put to use if they came back today.

D Pretend that you have been changed into a dinosaur. You are now a "___saurus." (Insert your name on the line, such as *Marcia-saurus* or *James-asaurus*.) Describe what you look like, what you eat, and how you spend your day.

P Would you want the dinosaurs to be around today? Write why or why not.

N Imagine that you found a dinosaur egg. Write a story telling what happened when the egg hatched.

N Scientists who study dinosaur fossils are called paleontologists. Write whether or not you would like to be a paleontologist.

Writing Frame

Dinosaurs!

Long ago,
(dinosaur name) (action),
(dinosaur name) (action),
(dinosaur name) (action),
And ruled the earth.

Dinosaurs!

Long ago,
Stegosaurus
waved its spiky tail,
Diplodocus stretched
its long neck,
Tyrannosaurus bared
its sharp teeth,
And ruled the earth.

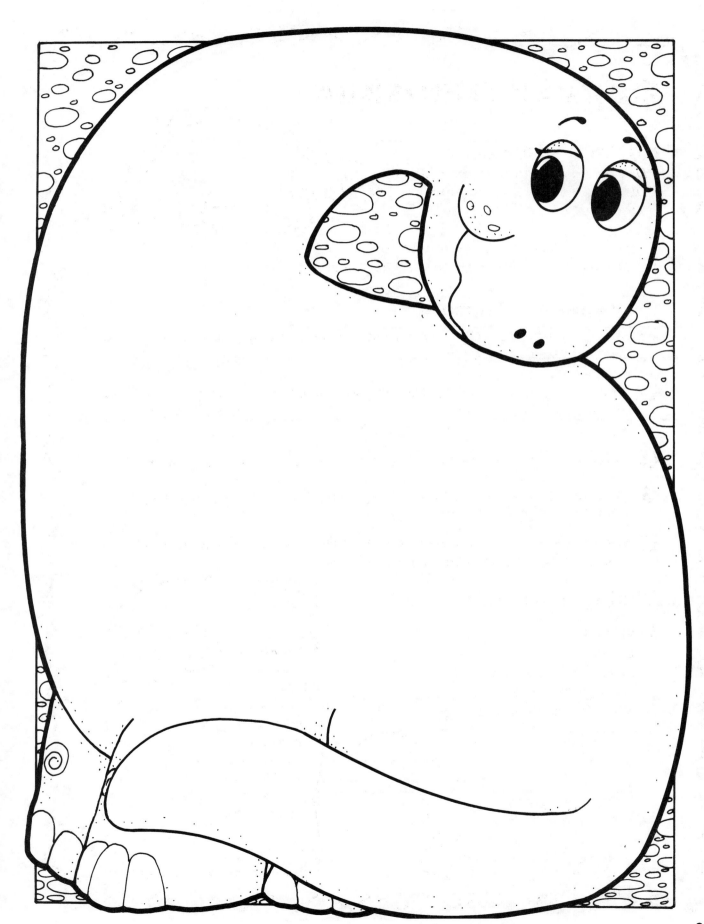

Writing Center Prompts © 2001 Creative Teaching Press

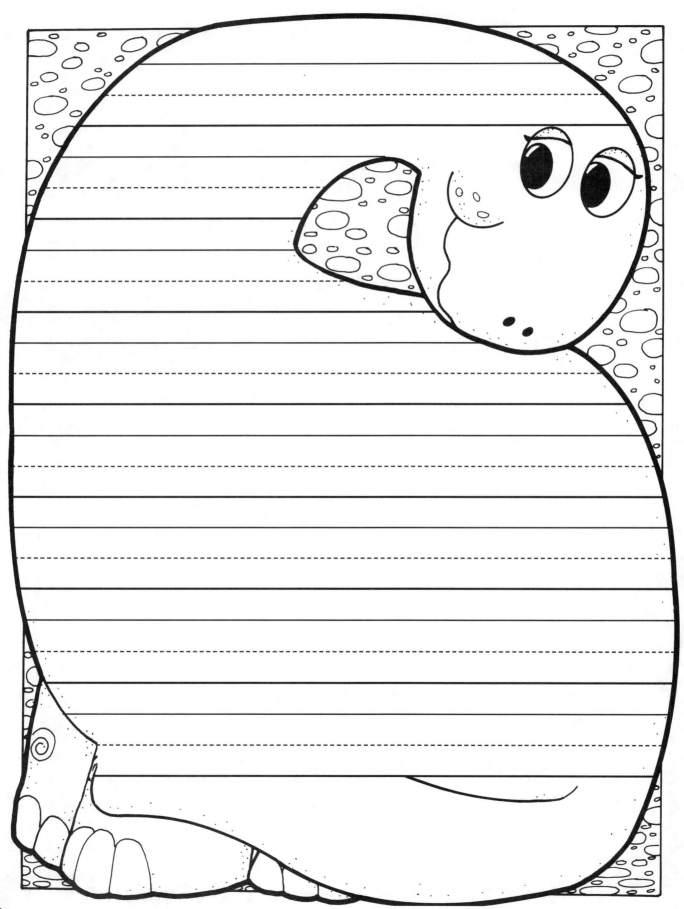

Writing Center Prompts © 2001 Creative Teaching Press